Collecting
Carlton Ware

© Francis Joseph Publications 1994

First Impression

Published in the UK by
Francis Joseph Publications
15 St Swithuns Road, London SE13 6RW. Tel: 081 318 9580

Distributed in the USA by Chilton Book Company, Radnor, Pennsylvannia

Typeset, printed and bound in Great Britain by
E J Folkard Print Services
199 Station Road, Crayford, Kent DA1 3QF

ISBN 1-870703-02-2

This book has been put together by the efforts of a small number of dedicated people, without whom the information, colour plates and listings in this book would not have been possible. They are sincerely thanked for their help and it is hoped that this publication does justice to their knowledge, co-operation and kindness. Many thanks.

They are:

Beverley and Beth   30 Church Street, London NW8
                               (071 262 1576)

Jayne Corbishley

Gilda Catlin   (0689) 852124

Andrew and Shani Fawcett

John Folkard   Typesetting (0322 526610)

Dennis Harwood

Trevor Leek   Studio Photography and cover
                               photograph (081 223 4440)

Francis Salmon   Production (081-318 9580)

Betty and Nevil Malin   Midlands Goss & Commemoratives,
                               The Old Cornmarket Antiques Centre,
                               Warwick (0926 495704)

Howard and Pat Watson   Art Deco Ceramics, The Courtyard,
                               Stratford-upon-Avon Antiques Centre
                               (0789 299524)

Mark Wilkinson   Christie's South Kensington, London
                               (071 321 3236)

Contents

Introduction   7

Carlton Ware — A Brief History   9

Pattern Names and Numbers   12

Decorating Techniques   22

Shapes   24

Backstamps and Other Methods of Dating   26

Pattern Dates — A General Guide   30

Starting a Carlton Ware Collection   97

Record Keeping   99

Insurance   100

Restoration   101

Lighting and Display   103

Rarity   104

Availability   105

Fakes and Reproductions   107

Antique Markets, Specialist Shops and Fairs   108

Auction Trends   109

Price and Rarity Guide   110

A Carlton Ware Chronology   114

Bibliography and Articles on Carlton Ware   116

Rouge Royale 1926

Handcraft 1929

1930

Handcraft 1929

Primitive 1930

Ovenlidsware

6

INTRODUCTION

In 1926, the *Pottery Gazette and Glass Trades Review* described Carlton Ware as "A firm whose forte lies in producing pottery that is characterised, first and foremost, by its decorative appeal", and this decorative appeal is the main attraction for collectors today.

Carlton Ware has been produced in a tremendous variety of ceramic forms over a full century and it is therefore not surprising that variety is also a major factor for collectors. The firm produced lustre ranges, floral embossed ware, crested china, advertising and promotional items, handcraft ware, china teaware, novelty cruets, luxury boxed coffee sets, figurines, ceramic animals, wall plaques and vases and salad ware. So it can be seen from illustrations in this book, that Carlton managed to produce successfully for both the cheaper, utility end, as well as for the luxurious, display only, end of the market

In the century of production, (for most of which it remained in the hands of the founding family) the products of the Carlton Ware factory clearly reflected a swift response to the design ideas of the day, this being especially noticeable in the contrast between pre-war and post-war decorative items.

For example, in the Art Deco period of the 1920s and 1930s, Carlton's luxury ranges mirrored the influences typical of the times, especially the archaeological discoveries in Egypt, interest in other civilisations like the Aztecs and the Byzantine Empire, the Jazz Age décor of Hollywood films and the vivid colours of contemporary art and ballet.

As well as many styles of decoration, many different methods of decoration were used, including lustre and gilding, print and enamel patterns, hand-painting, matt glazes and simple banded effects This gives the collector a wide selection from which to choose when focusing on Carlton for a collection.

China as well as earthenware was used, and the firm was probably the first to introduce, in 1929, oven-to-table ware. This was an innovation in those days.

The wide range of products and styles, coupled with a price range which runs from a few pounds to over a thousand, means that there is something to suit every collector.

Collectors of crested and commemorative ware and collectors of advertising items can look out for appropriate Carlton Ware products within their collections. Collectors of novelty cruets will also want to acquire both pre-war and post-war Carlton cruets which were produced in great variety.

While obviously the large and spectacular vases and plaques in the lustre ware range are expensive and are usually only found in specialist shops or in the London auction houses, the popular floral embossed ware of the 1930s and the newly collectable 1940s and 1950s items can often be found at very reasonable prices, though certain patterns, like the *Pink Buttercup* range, tend to fetch comparatively higher prices as do items like teapots and cups and saucers, which through use are more easily broken.

Because of their decorative qualities, Carlton Ware items even when designed for use as tableware were often kept for display only and so can be found in perfect condition. Another reason for their lasting appearance after so many years is that quality control at the factory was very high and stringent standards meant that the pottery glazes and decoration used were superior, so they have not deteriorated over the years.

It is important to note here that since at present Carlton Ware is still fairly readily obtainable, it is possible to reject any item with damage of any kind, and wait instead for a perfect piece to surface. Carlton Ware collecting is still in its infancy, with only one major auction house specialising in it (Christies), so you are still in a position to pick and choose for the time being.

Collections of Carlton Ware can look attractive in both modern and traditional settings and can be displayed according to the space available, many items such as leaf-shaped dishes are suitable either for wall display or on shelves.

It is still occasionally possible to find Carlton Ware at inexpensive outlets like flea-markets and charity shops, though this happens much less often than a few years ago, but at major antique fairs and specialist Art Deco fairs there are usually excellent displays and across the country specialist shops and stalls in antique centres and markets often have collectable items for sale and will contact collectors if they have items specially requested.

Because Carlton Ware in all its forms is in great demand, if collectors have pieces surplus to requirements it is usually possible to sell these, often at a profit.

Dating is much easier with Carlton Ware than with some other Staffordshire potteries as the backstamps are supplemented in many cases with shape numbers moulded into the base.

Though fakes as such are not yet a problem, the collector should be aware that genuine Carlton Ware moulds are being used subsequent to the closing of the factory, and it is important to check that the mould number and backstamp both indicate the appropriate year of production. Glazes, too, differ slightly and collectors will soon learn to detect the more recent productions.

A club for collectors is planned for the near future which will offer facilities for advertising items for sale or are wanted for a collection. It is hoped it will provide information about auctions, fairs and other events likely to be of interest. Please feel free to write to the publishers for free information and advice about these. A club already exists for New Zealand collectors, details of which are available from the Carlton Ware Collectors' Club, PO Box 90 – 771 Auckland, New Zealand.

CARLTON WARE – A BRIEF HISTORY

Established around 1890 at the Carlton Works, Stoke-on-Trent, the firm of Wiltshaw and Robinson was formed by a partnership of James Frederick Wiltshaw (1861-1918) and J. A. and H. T. Robinson. J. F. Wiltshaw was born in Burslem, Stoke-on-Trent and educated at the Newcastle Endowed School. His father worked for Macintyre & Co., of the Washington Works, Burslem, where later William Moorcroft was to start his career. J. P. Wiltshaw joined his father at Macintyre's, eventually becoming manager there, before founding the Carlton Ware factory. He died tragically after being severely injured in a rail accident at Stoke Station.

The firm was first registered in 1893, Carlton Ware becoming the factory's trade name the following year. Then, in 1906, china was added to the factory's output, and 'Carlton China' became an added trademark.

When in 1911 the partnership was dissolved, James Wiltshaw became the sole proprietor until his death in 1918, when his son, Frederick Cuthbert Wiltshaw, took over. A First World War pilot in the Flying Corps, he brought an enterprise and energy to his role that was to carry the factory into its most productive period.

Lustre wares, in a range of twelve colours, had become established as one of the main lines of the factory and in the early 1920s these were developed until they were unrivalled for variety and quality. Vases, bowls, ginger jars, wall plaques, dishes and pot pourri holders in classic shapes were decorated with patterns in the Egyptian, Byzantine, Persian, Aztec, Turkish, Japanese, Chinese and Art Deco styles, all tastefully gilded on rich lustre glazes of dark red, dark blue, deep green, pale blue, orange, pink, lime green, cream and black.

Motifs included birds of paradise, angel fish, waterlilies, butterflies, bluebirds, spiders' webs, sunbursts, fountains, weeping willow trees and lightning flashes.

In the mid-1920s novelty earthenware was introduced, including the cruets which were to remain characteristic of the firm throughout its history. Among these were jampots in the shape of fruit, small comical figurines and amusing napkin rings. Advertising and promotional material was made for firms like Guinness, (which is very collectable today). Small china commemorative and crested pieces were made in vast quantities, many of them being taken home as seaside holiday souvenirs.

In 1928 the firm of Birks, Rawlins & Co. of the Vine Pottery, Stoke, was taken over to allow for the expansion of china production, which led to new ranges of dainty print and enamel teaware in floral patterns like *Delphinium*, *Springtime* and *Sunshine*.

Salad ware also came into production about this time, and remained a range which continued until 1976, when regulations came into force prohibiting the use of lead paint so that the attractive brilliant red tomatoes and lobster claws were no longer available to decorate the salad bowls, salad servers, cress drainers, plates and dishes which had been popular for so long.

In August 1929 Carlton Ware introduced what was then a very innovative idea with their range of oven-to-table ware, easy to handle shapes decorated with simple banding in three colours, which the advertising claimed was "both utilitarian and ornamental", and could be plunged into cold water direct from the oven.

Most collectable of all the Carlton Ware earthenware ranges are the floral embossed ranges based on leaf and flower shapes. The *Oak Tree* range launched in 1934 in two colourways, blue (night) and cream (day) covered plaques, vases, jugs, candleholders, bookends, match-holders and cruets and was followed in 1935 by the *Garden Wall* range, similar in scope and, like the Oak Tree, matt glazed. In this way they were like the *Handcraft* range which was a matt-glazed and less expensive version of the luxury lustre range, and intended for customers who wanted decorative items in less costly materials.

The floral ranges which followed were highly glazed and in the main brightly coloured. These included *Buttercup,* popular in the naturalistic yellow and even more so in the pink, *Waterlily, Apple Blossom, Wild Rose, Foxglove, Primula* and *Poppy.*

A wide variety of tableware and decorative items were made in all these patterns and proved popular for gifts, especially the boxed sets which are still sometimes found complete with matching ceramic butter-knife or jam-spoon.

Some were based on the actual shape of the flower itself, as in *Waterlily* or *Buttercup,* while other ranges used leaf shapes with a spray of flowers as in the *Apple Blossom* and *Foxglove* ranges.

The very high standard of production was due to the stringent quality control standards set within the factory. The policy of the firm was that all decorators should be capable of dealing with everything produced by the factory, from a tiny dish to a twenty-four inch high vase.

Strict training schemes were in operation, since even skilled workers from elsewhere would need two or three years to learn the whole range and as much as ten years before total competency could be assumed. Working in the firm was often a family tradition and once trained, workers tended to remain there for the whole of their careers.

In order to make the most of their skilled workforce, Carlton Ware began a programme of expansion and modernisation immediately after the end of the Second World War, installing an electric glost kiln in 1945, an electric biscuit oven in 1948 and an infra-red dryer in 1955 which cut drying time from three-quarters of an hour to ten minutes.

Post-war ranges were drastically re-styled to account for the tastes of the 1950s. Sophistication rather than prettiness was now called for, leading to leaf-shapes in twin-tone colours – brown/cream, two-tone grey, twin-tone green, and twin-tone Chartreuse. There were also "Windswept" shapes in combinations of dusky pink and pale blue, glossy bottle green and glossy pale blue, and matt brown and cream. These suited post-war taste, along with smart motifs like hazel-nuts and coffee-beans. What flowers there were tended to be more exotic than before – convulvulus and orchids, for instance – on lime green, pale mauve or sharp pink backgrounds.

After the successful period of the 1950s and early 1960s the firm was, like many of the smaller factories, taken over, in this case by the empire of Arthur Wood and Sons in 1967. Anthony F. Wood became the new managing director, with Angela Fox as designer.

Under the new regime, Carlton Ware's export trade, always a major factor in its success, rose rapidly by as much as seventy-five per cent. Another twenty years followed, with fruit as a theme replacing the pre-war flowers and tableware in novelty shapes like the *Walking Ware* range, with its colourful striped socks and strap shoes attracting press publicity. Designed by Roger Mitchell and Danka Napiorkowska, it was made by Carlton Ware under licence from 1975, and other novelties were made in collaboration with Fluck and Law, of 'Spitting Image' fame.

Despite its many successes, the recession of the early 1980s hit Carlton Ware, like many other firms, very hard. For two years it was in the hands of a holding company, County Potteries plc, before being taken into receivership in March 1989. A rescue bid was launched by Grosvenor Ceramic Hardware, of Stone in Staffordshire, a centenary vase being produced in 1990, along with lustre ware ranges and novelty teapots. Unfortunately, the momentum had been lost, and production of Carlton Ware finally ceased in the autumn of 1992, leaving collectors with just over a century's high quality products from which to choose. Already specialist auctions of Carlton Ware are being held, and more and more collectors are beginning to agree with the factory motto of Wiltshaw and Robinson – "Buy Carlton – first with the latest and the best!"

PATTERN NAMES AND NUMBERS

As with many potteries of the 1920s and 1930s, pattern books giving full pattern descriptions are not at present available, and so, again as with many other potteries, collectors have given their own names to many patterns. As these can vary, perhaps the best way of identifying a pattern is by the pattern number. What follows is not a complete list but one which covers most of the more familiar patterns, likely to be encountered at auctions or for sale in specialist shops or stalls. The publisher would appreciate any pattern numbers not given here to be forwarded to them.

It is important to remember that the same pattern was often used on several different background colours, so that one number will appear on more than one ground colour.

If an invented name has been given to a certain pattern, it appears alongside the description.

624	Traditional **Imari** pattern with floral panels, base marked "Reproduction Swansea China".
1143	Powder blue ground with Egyptian motifs (this number possibly 3143)
1855	Matt pale green ground, bird of paradise on stylised plant. **Long-tailed bird.**
1981	Carnations on a blue ground.
2006	Black ground with coloured and gilt dragons.
2030	Matt black ground with pink and green blossom sprays.
2031	Pink ground, birds on prunus blossom, chrysanthemums and good luck symbols. **Kien Lung.**
2144	Matt blue background with exotic drooping trees.
2216	Blue ground with figures in temple.
2270	Black ground, oriental couple among pagodas, terraces.
2281	Matt black ground with cockerel and flowers.
2359	Powder blue ground Chinoiserie pagodas and bridges with oriental ladies. Matt finish, early pattern.
2364	Powder blue ground, oriental ladies among pagodas and bridges.
2428	Deep blue lustre ground, Chinoiserie figures, pagodas and bridges.
2470	Matt black ground with Chinoiserie figures, pagodas and bridges.
2519	Blue ground, Chinoiserie in gilt.
2655	Orange, brown, yellow and black in a graph design. **Geometric.**
2710	Powder blue ground with Egyptian motifs. **Tutenkhamen.**
2728	Deep blue ground *Chinoiserie* pagodas and bridges. Probably most common Chinoiserie pattern
2729	Deep blue ground, pagodas and a junk before a bridge.

2822 Deep blue ground, storks in garden scene.

2825 Oriental ladies, pagodas and bridges, various grounds.

2880 Coral ground with black, Chinoiserie pagodas, bridges and terraces.

2881 Black ground, tan frieze with Chinoiserie, pagodas and bridges. Frequently seen.

2884 Royal blue ground, Egyptian design of figures in a temple.

2914 Black ground with jade green banding, heavily decorated with gilt oriental scenes.

2917 Matt black exterior, vivid orange interior, for coffee set.

2929 Powder blue ground, Chinoiserie pagodas and bridges, matt finish, clearly pattern.

2932b Two Cranes drinking, one from a pool the other standing on one foot.

2944 Orange ground with central medallion showing two silhouetted children playing with bubbles.

2948 Complex Chinoiserie design with pagodas, bridges, boats and figures. Orange ground. **Chinaland.**

2950 Pagoda in colours and gilt on dark blue ground.

2972 Deep blue ground, Chinoiserie pagodas and bridges, with six figures.

2975 Matt peach lustre ground, flowers and foliage tube – lined in orange, green, blue and yellow.

3015 Mottled red ground, mountains, trees, terraces and pagoda in natural colours. **Chinaland.**

3025 Blue lustre ground, butterflies and spiders' webs in delicate gilt.

3026 As 2728 with white/cream ground.

3026b Colours and gilt on vellum, exotic birds and trees.

3041 Blue lustre ground, apples and blossom.

3050 Blue ground, Persian style flowers and foliage.

3064 Orange ground with fruit clusters and blossom

3073 Deep blue background, stylised swallows and abstract designs in colours and gilt.

3141 Cream ground, bluebirds flying by trees in a landscape.

3142 Pink ground with spiders web and stylised flowers.

3143 Mottled black and deep pink ground, exotic birds and foliage.

3144 Mottled light blue long-tailed birds in an exotic landscape, gilt embellishment.

3145 Coral ground, gilt dragon on black medallion, gilt and coloured frieze at base.

3154 Mottled orange ground, birds of paradise flying past stylised foliage.

3158 As 3154 with deep blue ground.

3188 Mottled red ground, stylised flowers and foliage.

3179 Rust coloured ground with oriental figures and pagoda on a black panel. Elaborate gilt and coloured frieze.

3190 Red ground with cross-shaped medallion of stylised flowers and berries, with two butterflies in black and white.

3195 Orange lustre ground, stylised flowers and butterflies.

3197 Blue ground with colours and gilt, exotic birds and flowers.

3199 Ladies before pagodas on a blue ground, gilded.

3236 Bluebells and other flowers on a blue ground in shades of yellow. blue, green and lavender. *Handcraft.*

3237 Deep blue ground with dominant dragon, in gilt and colours.

3242 Matt glaze, blue, yellow and lavender stylised cornflowers

3244 Matt glaze, blue ground, exotic trees and clouds in blue lavender, orange and gilt. **Fantasia.**

3352 Lightning flashes and bubbles on grounds of orange or red. **Jazz.**

3255 Central floral medallion with star containing irises, fan shapes and floral motifs in mauve, blue, green, yellow, and black. *Handcraft.*

3275 Orange ground, bird of paradise flying over stylised foliage.

3278 Royal blue ground with gilt stylised honesty in violet, green and orange.

3279 Pale blue ground with birds flying among exotic trees and plants.

3281 Speckled cream ground with birds and exotic trees.

3297 Pink ground, diagonal panels of flowers and chevrons, patterned borders. *Handcraft.*

3331 Matt green ground with dragon in gilt and colours.

3332 A dragon attacking stylised bats.

3352 Mottled dark red ground with lighting flashes and bubbles motifs.

3353 Mottled orange ground with lightning flashes in shades of green, blue and black.

3354 Matt blue glaze, bird of paradise on stylised blossom bough.

3356 Lightning motif in light and dark blue, bronze, copper lustre and gilt, for coffee set.

3387 Matt green or blue ground, with three interlocking posies of stylised flowerheads linked by lightning flashes. **Sunburst.**

3388 Matt pale blue ground, swallows flying among exotic bushes and trees.

3406 Dark blue ground, green long-tailed swallows above exotic plants. **Melon.**

3421 Powder blue ground with long-tailed birds hovering above exotic plants and flowers.

3438 Stylised foliage in mauve, blue yellow and black, with navy horizontal lines. *Handcraft.*

3449 Mottled red ground with geometric band of foliage and flowers.

3451 Crinoline lady with parasol strolling on garden terrace, shades of blue, orange, yellow and cream, rose bush to left of figure. **Crinoline Lady**. *Handcraft.*

3452 Dark blue ground with butterflies and star-shaped floral clusters.

3476 Mottled yellow and green ground, stylised tree casting a shadow.

3478 Mottled orange ground with colourful bands of stylised hollyhocks. **Hollyhocks.**

3501 Mottled brown ground with sprays of coloured stylised flowers.

3505 Mottled orange ground with trees by a lily pond in purple, blue, orange, white, black and gilt.

3508 Cream and blue ground with flowers and foliage in colours. *Handcraft.*

3517 Tableware pattern of stylised trees in orange, green, yellow and black on a pale yellow ground.

3522 Ice blue ground with black and grey boughs, pink flowers.

3524 Matt ground with branches and Autumn leaves.

3525 Mottled yellow ground with large bird of paradise among exotic flowers. **Bird of Paradise.**

3526 Foxgloves and other stylised flowers in blue, pink, green, and black. *Handcraft.*

3530 Mottled red ground, with exotic oriental bird perched on a waterlily. **Exotic Bird on Waterlily.**

3536 Mottled red ground with ornamental flowers and bird.

3544 Mottled orange ground, birds of paradise and stylised flowerheads.

3557 Deep blue ground, exotic circular flowerheads with behind a fan of colourful panels, green yellow, orange and mauve, with gilding.

3558 Mottled red ground, exotic circular flowerheads fronting a fan of coloured panels, yellow, green, orange and blue, with clouds of dots and gilding.

3562 Black and aquamarine ground with stylised flowers and bird-in-song.

3570 Matt turquoise glaze with rectangles and chevrons in black, red, yellow, mauve and green. Bauhaus in style.

3588 Mottled dark pink ground, fan motif above stylised flowerheads in colours and gilt.

3595 Sky blue ground, dragon confronting a traveller, colours and gilt, matt glaze.

3601 Blue ground with floral clusters in colours, mainly pinks and greens, and gilt.

3606 Green ground overlaid in bright yellows with flowers and butterflies.

3645 Ladies before pagodas and bridges, highlighted in gilt on mottled red ground.

3648   White ground with sprays of stylised cornflowers and vertical stripes, shades of blue, yellow and lavender. *Handcraft.*

3651   Ground of blue, green and purple teardrops with stylised circular flowerheads and angular panels in black, yellow orange, fawn and gilt.

3654   Black ground with gilt chinoiserie of a couple beneath a tree.

3655   Geometric pattern in orange, brown, yellow and black, in chevrons, circles and grids in graph-like formation.

3657   Geometric design in shades of black and green with gilt.

3663   Black reserve with vivid multi-coloured flowers with stems and leaves.

3675   Primrose ground with two oriental figures under blossom. Highly ornate friezes with flowers in gilt and colours.

3691   Shaded light green ground with aster-like flowers in yellow, pink and orange with dark green leaves.

3692   Tangerine ground slashed with black, white and gilt lightning flashes. *Handcraft.*

3693   Dark blue reserve, with daisy-like flowers in shades of yellow, orange, pink and white, with stems and light green leaves. *Handcraft.*

3694   Mottled orange reserve with multi-coloured flowers in mauve, yellows and pinks with leaves in shades of yellow, green and bottle-green.

3696   Dark blue ground with stylised palm fronds and flowers in colours and gilt, Egyptianesque in style. **Egyptian Fan.**

3699   Orange ground, exotic flowers held by fan-shaped motifs and curved lines.

3703   Flowers and trees in pink, orange, blue green and gilt.

3714   Matt green ground with gum tree design.

3719   Primrose ground overliad with embossed floral decoration.

3765A Turquoise ground with exotic flowers in colours and gilt beneath a tree laden with eye motifs as blossoms.

3769   Yellow ground, Mephistopheles figure dressed in bright red, in a tropical landscape with exotic flowers, bushes and a tree with pendulous foliage heavy with blossom, banded with swags of berries in orange, green, red and white. **Mephistopheles.**

3774   Cream ground with multi-coloured stylised flowers held by curving lines.

3785   Matt pale blue ground with harebells and flowerheads in colours and gilt.

3786   Mottled green ground with large stylised flowerheads, slashed with pink covered with small flowerheads.

3789   As 3790 with powder blue ground.

3790   Mottled green and yellow ground, decorated with sprays of pink flowers and seed-pods.

3794   Matt sage green ground with highly stylised flowers and leaves.

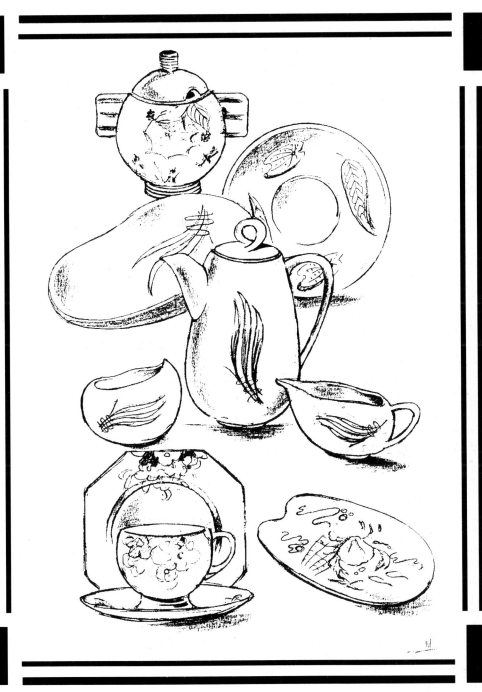

3802 Brown and yellow ground with basketweave design and bands of coloured flowers and foliage.

3814 Mottled red ground with stylised flowerheads and foliage in colours and gilt.

3818 Mottled lime green ground with hollyhocks in shades of pink and red, with circular pale green leaves.

3819 Mottled blue ground with stylised flowers and foliage in gilt and colours.

3820 As 3819 with black ground.

3860 Pale green ground with stylised tree, bushes and flowers in foreground, path leading to garden gate in background with bushes.

3890 Pale mauve ground, flame-shaped pastel-coloured plants below, ragged foliage hanging from above, exotic bird flying past.

3907 Pale blue ground lustre, exotic bird in flight.

3913 Kingfisher flying past willow tree.

3894 Matt green ground, sprays of exotic foliage.

3913 Abstract flower in blue, yellow and brown.

3917 Running pattern in shades of lemon, pale blue and turquoise on cream.

3945 Matt cream ground with gum tree design.

3950 Shaded cream ground, exotic flowerheads in colours and gilt.

3966 Green ground, tree in shades of green with hydrangea blossom in colours and gilt.

3971 Primrose ground, flowing seabed colours, ornamental fish.

3972 Orange lustre ground with stylised flowers and foliage in colours.

3973 Green ground with stylised flowers and foliage in colours.

3974 Exotic highly decorated fish in delicate, flowering seabed scene.

3986 Cream ground, stylised flowers and foliage in colours and gilt.

3989 Blue ground, mottled exotic tree with pendant foliage and blossoms like eye motifs, bushes and plants below. **Tiger Tree.**

4017 As 4018 with orange ground.

4018 Red ground with tree, exotic bird standing nearby, in colours and gilt.

4103 Green ground traced with gilt cobwebs, fruiting branch above, harebells below.

4108 Pale green ground, with kingfisher flying past a willow tree, in gilt and colours.

4160 Green ground below, vivid blue above, with exotic birds flying past a twisted exotic tree with fans of blossom, gilded, black shadows.

4163 Shaded yellow ground, broad black tree-trunk with green foliage and red blossoms.

4186 Light blue ground with hens pecking at a bouquet of flowers, colours and gilt.

4219 Sprays of realistically-depicted anemones with foliage in colours on very pale green ground.

4243 Grey ground, embossed flowers and spider's web.

4247 Orange ground, black silhouetted trees and grass with light green foliage, rabbits playing shown in black silhouette. **Shadow Bunny.**

4249 Blue ground, with butterflies flying among flower-laden branches in colours.

4340 Exotic wading birds grazing in water under trees, in colours and gilt on deep red ground. *Rouge Royale.*

4434 Blue ground with Chinoiserie decoration of ladies before pagodas and bridges. in colours and gilt.

4519 Black ground with oriental couple under trees, in gilt and colours.

4906 Primrose shading to cream ground with floral decoration in colours and gilt.

5859 Mottled pink ground, shades of green and black forming silhouette scene of rabbits playing under a tree.

Other pattern names in use

Cherry A Handcraft pattern, matt glaze in deep blue with pink streamers and yellow and red cherry-like fruits.

Geometric Sunflower Fantasy flowers resembling sunflowers in a bouquet.

Nightingale Vivid green/blue background with black panel on which a bird on a twig sings above hollyhocks and other flowers in vivid colours.

Lily of the Valley Sprays of white, bell-shaped flowers on a black ground.

Blush Ware The pattern name is usually given on the base, generally being the name of the flower.

Floral Embossed Ware Similarly, the pattern name is taken from the flower, but here the background colour is often added – Green Foxglove, Yellow Foxglove, etc. When two names have been used for one pattern, as with "Oak Tree" and "Acorn", it is usually clear that the same pattern is meant by both names.

DECORATING TECHNIQUES

In its early years, Carlton Ware output resembled that of other factories of the period like Fielding's Crown Devon and Royal Worcester, reflecting the taste of the day for delicate hand-painted or transferware floral decoration on pale green or buff backgrounds with gilt edging.

Similarly, blue and white patterns like the familiar **Willow Tree** were popular and some teaware was patterned in white on black. Pewter and EPNS. mounts, handles and lids were sometimes added.

Lustre Ware was also popular, one range in orange lustre being decorated with a pattern of swallows, the swallow being part of the Carlton factory's trademark from the early years until around 1927.

At the factory, twelve strong, vibrant colours were developed for the lustre ranges and these became the mainstay of the factory's reputation between the wars. Because of the complexity of the process, lustre was restricted to the luxury end of the factory's output. Lustre glazes use a combination of resin and oil with metallic salts and are applied to the ware before firing, the aim being either to create the appearance of precious metal on the surface or to give an iridescent appearance.

Silver, gold, titanium and platinum, plus some base metals, were also used, sometimes in combination with each other, and could produce such colours as ruby, bronze, green and mother-of-pearl with many variations according to the temperature at which the firing took place.

Painted on free-hand, the lustre was applied evenly to the ware in exactly the right amount, since too much or too little would produce a poor result. Any contamination of the surface would create blemishes, so great care was taken to avoid dust or accidental marks. Firing was at low temperatures in a reducing or oxygen-starved atmosphere, very carefully controlled to avoid under- or over-firing.

Vases and similar items like pot pourri holders often had mother-of-pearl interiors, derived from a titanium compound. Background colours were sometimes given the effect of marbling, or were mottled, bubbled or splashed by treating the surface before firing with a spattering of turpentine, light or heavy, according to the effect desired.

After firing, the ware was decorated with one of the many spectacular patterns for which inspiration was drawn from other eras and other civilisations – China and Japan, with oriental figures, pagodas and temples, Persia with mosques and minarets, Egypt with the newly-discovered treasures of Tutenkhamen, the Aztecs and the Byzantine empire. Fairyland contributed another source of inspiration, with fountains, butterflies, spiders' webs, dragonflies, birds of paradise and enchanted castles. Art Deco motifs included flames, fans, lightning flashes, shooting stars and sunbursts. Enamelled paint and gilding were used to enrich the surface of the ware, sometimes adding texture whilst at the same time, hiding any tiny flaws which might, in spite of all precautions, have occurred during the firing process.

Other techniques were applied to Carlton Ware's less expensive ranges. "Print and enamel" patterns were used on their dainty china tea-services, the outlines being laid down by means of a transfer and the colour being applied by hand, giving a crisp, lively effect. Most Staffordshire potteries used this method for some ranges, including Shelley, Susie Cooper and Clarice Cliff.

Hand-painting provided the detail for Carlton's many novelty ranges. After the background material had been fired, the petals, stamens and stems were added to the floral embossed ware before re-firing at a low temperature.

Transfer-printing was used for several ranges, including crested items – some of which were available in mother-of-pearl lustre – and advertising ware, when the trade logos of firms like Guinness, Trophy Bitter, Bass & Co, Mackeson, Haig and smaller firms were applied to promotional items.

Carlton's oven-to-table ware was given a semi-matt glaze with wavy banding in three colours. Made of a special fire-resistant body, the range was guaranteed to survive undamaged even if plunged into cold water straight from a hot oven. Common place now, this was a novelty in 1929 when the range was launched. The semi-matt glaze was also used on decorative items in the Handcraft range. This was also introduced at the end of the 1920s as tastes changed and retailers sought more subtle ornamental ware for their customers, to complement the more subdued soft furnishings which were then in fashion.

Since Carlton Ware aimed largely at the gift market, presentation was an important consideration. Some items like coffee sets were made available in satin-lined boxes or complete with wicker carrying trays, while floral embossed ware such as jam or butter dishes complete with ceramic spoons or knives to match could be boxed ready for gift-wrapping.

Occasionally limited editions were produced to commemorate special anniversaries and these were each individually hand-painted and numbered. They now fetch high prices at auction.

SHAPES

Perhaps the most versatile of all the Staffordshire potteries in the sheer range and diversity of its shapes, Carlton Ware began with two strands of production, the conventional and the classical. The conventional was tableware and related items and the shapes used, like the decoration itself, were very similar to those of neighbouring factories like Fielding's Crown Devon and Royal Worcester.

Classical shapes were used for the luxury lustre ware range, depending for their effect on clean, simple lines so that the superb glazes and complex patterns were paramount. Restrained touches of gilding on handles and (in the case of ginger jars, pot pourri holders and powder-bowls) the knobs of lids added a tasteful emphasis to the elegant shapes, some of which followed the style of Chinese pottery.

In the 1920s, like most other firms, Carlton Ware felt the need to add variety and novelty to their shape range and here the first signs were shown of the inventive wit and sense of humour which was to appear increasingly in the decades to come. Jam-pots in the shape of fruit, novelty cruets and salad ware moulded with tomatoes or lobster claws as feet or as decorative detail enlivened the Carlton Ware range and created interest in the trade press.

Before the end of the decade the firm was also winning praise for their *Handcraft* range, in which the shapes were similar to but slightly chunkier than the range of shapes used for the expensive lustre ware.

The early 1930s saw the launching of imaginative shapes derived from the countryside, the *Oak Tree* range and the *Garden Wall* range. The *Oak Tree*, with its background either beige (**Day**) or grey/blue (**Night**), featured a gnarled oak tree with green and orange foliage and outsize acorns, and the variety of shapes seemed endless – plaques, jugs, vases, bowls, bookends, dishes, match-holders, toastracks, candlesticks, biscuit barrels and cruets, providing a rich field for today's collector.

The *Garden Wall* range, also in beige or blue, was moulded to look like rustic brickwork with a colourful 'cottage garden' border of flowers, decorating jugs, vases, bowls, dishes, and other items. Again, this range displays effectively as a collection, including as it does a wide variety of shapes all featuring the same pattern scaled up or down and ingeniously adapted to the surface available.

Oak Tree and *Garden Wall* were both matt glazed and the *Fruit Basket* range is, in contrast, very highly glazed. With cream or green as the background colour, the ware is moulded to resemble basket-work, the decoration being bands of brightly-coloured fruit in low relief. The shapes used are traditional wide-necked jugs and shallow dishes, with novelty items like toastracks, cruets and sauce-boats also included.

The mid 1930s saw the development of the embossed floral ware range, and this decoration also included moulded berries and leaves. Some ranges, like *Buttercup* in pink or yellow and *Waterlily* used the actual shape of the flower as the shape of the article, while other ranges like *Apple Blossom* or *Foxglove* were moulded as leaves for the main body of the shape, with the addition of a flower or spray of blossom for the decoration. Again the background colour was cream or green, this time a much paler green than in the *Fruit Basket* range.

At the end of the decade and during the wartime years when most of the decorated ware produced was restricted to export only, we saw the emergence of patterns like **Foxglove**, **Spring-time**, **Primula**, **Wild Rose**, and **Hydrangea**. Again, all manner of shapes were available, from teapots and other tableware to decorative items like baskets and bowls.

With the radical change in post-war tastes, shapes were re-designed to satisfy the demand for clear-cut, unfussy outlines. Just as colours became more sophisticated with twin-tone combinations and acid greens, sharp pinks and mauves, so the shapes used became streamlined and windswept, bearing moulded motifs like convulvulus, magnolia and hazelnut.

As always, novelties were popular and just as the 1930s had seen Carlton Ware offering a bouquet of flowers for the table, now fruit became the theme and teaware, jam-pots, cruets and serving dishes took the form of apples, pears and even lemons.

Gradually novelty items began to take preponderance in the Carlton Ware catalogue, so that the *Walking Teaset* seemed a natural progression and as it developed in ever more outrageous shapes it was happily accepted along with all the other Carlton Ware extravagances, be it toastracks in the shape of a sliced loaf, a cruet made to look like a bowtie or a giant mushroom, or a teapot shaped like the Red Baron's aeroplane.

Ornamental ware, of course, continued alongside the factory's more frivolous aspect, culminating in the Centenary Vase of 1990, by which time many changes of fortune had heralded the closing of the factory and the disappearance – though perhaps not the final disappearance? – of Carlton Ware from the pottery scene.

Backstamps and Other Methods of Dating

Apart from the early **Blush Ware**, which closely resembles similar items produced by several contemporary potteries, in general Carlton Ware is easily recognisable, though occasionally Crown Devon lustre items may be mistaken for Carlton Ware lustre at first sight.

Shape is often the first visual clue to dating an item as, though some shapes were used for several decades (the leaf for instance), they were modified in line with popular taste and a pre-war item will be in outline quite different from a post-war item, even if the basic subject of the shape is the same.

Colour is similarly a good rough guide to the dating of an item, since post-war colours tend in general to be much bolder than pre-war colours, apart from the lustre ware which inevitably made full use of the complete colour spectrum for its effects.

It is impossible to be arbitrary about dating, since with Carlton Ware in particular, several backstamps seem to have been used concurrently, while many patterns were made over a prolonged period during which a variety of backstamps could have been used.

Shape numbers impressed on the base of items would appear to be the most useful method of dating, since they indicate the relative age of the items being compared, but owing to the irregular base area of some items some have no impressed shape numbers, while in other cases, though the intention was to impress a number, for various reasons this proved only partially successful and the finished result is blurred or incomplete, so that it is impossible to decipher it with total accuracy. Again, moulds were used over a period of years, so the start and finish of the production period needs to be known and taken into account along with the backstamp and its period of use.

While in some cases it is known roughly when a pattern began and ended, a number of patterns were produced concurrently, so that it is not possible to calculate the number of items of any one single pattern during that period.

Occasionally it is possible to date an item with almost total accuracy by reference to its provenance. If an item was bought for a particular occasion such as a wedding anniversary, a birthday or a presentation, it is likely to have been purchased new, not long before that date from a shop continuously replenishing its stock direct from the factory.

Early Carlton Ware included **Blush Ware**, **Lustre Ware** (including some lustre tableware) and conventional tableware, some patterns being made as Carlton China and so marked.

Decorative lustre ware continued after the First World War, as did china tableware, but novelty earthenware began to make its mark and in August,

Backstamps

c1890

1894 onwards
with some
variations

1906
onwards

KANG.HSI
1662 — 1722
c.
1914

Carlton Ware
MADE IN ENGLAND
"TRADE MARK"

1925+

Carlton China
MADE IN ENGLAND

1925-57

Wiltshaw and
Robinson mark
1927

Carlton Ware
MADE IN ENGLAND
"TRADE MARK"

RTN° 754801

Script mark 1930-34

Carlton Ware
MADE IN ENGLAND
"TRADE MARK"
REGISTERED
AUSTRALIAN DESIGN
REGISTRATION APPLIED FOR

Script mark 1925-45

Carlton Ware
Handpainted
MADE IN ENGLAND
"TRADE MARK"
REGISTERED
AUSTRALIAN DESIGN

Script mark 1945

Carlton Ware
MADE IN ENGLAND
"TRADE MARK"

Late script mark

*Retitled CARLTON WARE LTD from January 1958

1926 the *Pottery Gazette and Glass Trade Review* praised the factory for producing "decorative lines for table use for different purposes in different seasons", including salad ware – "a lettuce and tomato dish . . . a lobster dish" and "a grapefruit holder", "a cucumber dish and a cress dish and plate and a preserve pot which readily reminds one of the growing fruit", a fruit set and "a series of tomato cruet pieces". All these were in addition to items for "the wedding present trade", described as "morning sets and coffee sets in lustred decoration, fitted to wicker trays with wooden bases".

Exactly three years later, in August 1929, praise was again being lavished on Carlton Ware for a "style of pottery decoration which will fit in with the neater styles of furnishings" – *Handcraft Ware* – and Carlton *Ovenware*, was an innovative range of oven-to-table ware carrying a year's guarantee against breakage.

Impressed numbers in the hundreds indicated production in the very early 1930s for *Fruit Basket* items, followed by *Oak Trees* in the eleven hundreds and *Garden Wall* in the twelve hundreds, probably indicating 1934/35, with **Buttercup**, in yellow and pink, running from 1936 to 1945 in the 1395 to 2046 range (intermittently only, of course – other patterns were being produced and given adjacent numbers simultaneously) **Waterlily** (nos. 1540 to 1902) and **Apple Blossom** (1614 to 2008) were in production from 1936 to 1940, with **Wild Rose** making its appearance in 1939, in the seventeen hundreds. **Foxglove** began the following year in the late 1800s, with **Primula** making a briefer appearance in 1943. By 1945 the numbers had reached 2000 and the change-over to post-war shapes was about to begin.

By 1958 the *Pottery Gazette and Glass Trade Review* was praising the 'Leaf' and the 'Windswept' shapes, both available in twin-tone colours. Motifs included Hazelnuts, Convulvulus and Magnolia, and before long fruit shapes were to come into their own, with impressed marks reaching 2694 by 1967.

Changes in patterns were matched by changes in backstamps. From 1890 a curved ribbon carried the initials W & R with a swallow flying above. From 1894 a circle, with a swallow in the centre, has the wording 'W & R Stoke on Trent' with a crown above and 'Carlton Ware' below. This mark, with variations, continued till around 1927, 'Made in England' being added in the early 1900s. A similar mark was used for Carlton China.

The next mark began the familiar series of 'Carlton Ware' in script, the bar of the 't' joining the starting-point of the 'w'. Below this the words "Made in England", with 'Trade Mark' below that, were in block letters, making a mark which continued till around 1935.

The mark which followed was in use until the end of the war, and has created some confusion, as, though it was in essence the same as the preceding mark it had the words, "Registered Australian Design" added. This was simply to deter the copying of exported items, and did not, as has sometimes been thought, indicate a design originating in Australia.

After the war a much smaller script mark was used, all reference to Australia being eliminated, and after the takeover by Woods, block letters were used for some items, as for example the *Walking Ware* Teaset, which has in block letters, upper and lower case, 'Carlton Ware England Lustre Design' in three lines.

During its final years, a tiny script mark was used, easily recognisable as it is considerably smaller than any other previous mark.

Sometimes additional wording – 'Handcraft', 'Rouge Royale' etc, offers a further clue to dating.

By a judicious mixture of observation of backstamps and impressed numbers plus a shrewd assessment of shape and colour, it is possible to calculate the probable date of most Carlton Ware items, though as with all the Staffordshire potteries, surprises abound, so it is best not to be too dogmatic and to accept that it is unlikely, at this late date, that total accuracy in all cases is going to be possible. Knowledge adds enormously to enjoyment, but all collectors, whatever they collect, need to beware of the danger of becoming obsessive over details.

PATTERN DATES – A GENERAL GUIDE

1890-c1918 – **Blush Ware** in a wide variety of patterns, mainly floral, with touches of gilding and sometimes electro-plated mounts. Similar ware in blue and white.

1890-c1940 – Conventional tableware, some with lustre glazes. *Swallows* were a frequent motif.

1906-1940 approx. Carlton China – floral patterns on china tableware, greatly expanded from 1928 when the purchase of Birks, Rawlins and Company made available their premises at the Vine Pottery for increased china production.

1890-c1940 – Crested souvenir ware produced for the seaside trade, plus commemorative items for royal and other occasions, both made in a wide range and vast quantities.

1890-c1992 – **Lustre Ware** produced in a wide range of colours and patterns, *Rouge Royale* persisting throughout as particularly popular. Here the style of decoration gives an approximate guide to the date of production, especially when taken into account along with details of shape – twisted Art Nouveau handles, for instance, indicating an earlier period, sharp finned flanges a later period. Similarly, elaborate metal mounting also presupposes a date prior to the First World War, reflecting as it does the taste of customers of the Edwardian age, as do realistic sprays of flowers depicted in a rather fussy style with formal borders.

The 1920s brought in new motifs, from the Egyptian hieroglyphics which became fashionable following the excavations of the tomb of Tutenkhamen in 1922, to the Jazz Age lightning flashes which followed the stylistic revolution of the 1925 Paris exhibition of decorative arts.

Oriental motifs resulted from the vogue for the 'Mysterious East' which was also reflected in early films and popular music. An impression that China and Japan consisted entirely of pagodas, temples, bridges and terraces with quaintly-dressed people taking tea resulted in many patterns consisting of imaginary landscapes reflecting this view.

Dreamscapes of exotic birds flying through groves of convoluted trees and elaborate flowers were used throughout the 1920s and 1930s and appeared not only on vases, bowls and ginger jars but also on coffee sets, many of them luxuriously boxed in satin-lined coffrets or supplied with wicker trays. While it would be an over-simplification to suggest that pattern numbers can be equated as applying from 1000 to 2500 prior to 1920, 2500 to 3500 as covering the 1920s and 3500 to 4500 as covering the 1930s, this does give a very rough guide when the following pattern numbers are taken into account.

Pattern number, 2710 – Tutenkhamen, with Egyptian motifs.

Pattern number 3352 – Jazz, with lightning flashes

Pattern number 3236 – A Handcraft pattern. Handcraft began in 1929

1926-1976 – Salad Ware was made in a wide variety of shapes and motifs, including tomato decoration and lobster claws for feet and for the finials of salad servers. Some items were made with electro-plated mounts. The range remained popular throughout and came to an end owing to new government Health and Safety legislation regarding the lead content of red paint, which meant the vivid red of the tomatoes was no longer available.

At the same time, novelty tableware was introduced, including jampots in fruit shapes and novelty cruets. Around this time, advertising ware was produced for a variety of clients of whom Guinness was a leading household name.

1929 – This year marked the introduction of **Carlton Ovenware**, a range of oven-to-tableware decorated with wavy coloured bands. Despite the advertising assurances of its durability, none of this is known to have survived.

Handcraft Ware was also introduced around this time and was made for several years, being produced in a range of subtle colour combinations, described by the *Pottery Gazette and Glass Trade Review* as "cutting out the high lights that were associated with the brilliantly glazed and lustred pottery". They called the new range "truly decorative and at once impressive", praising the "elimination of detail" and "the massing of chunks of ornament".

1930+ Fruit Basket range. **Oak Tree** (or **Acorn**) range.

c1934/5 – Garden Wall range.

1936 – Gradual introduction of the floral embossed ranges, added to as dictated by demand and in production for as long as popular. **Buttercup** (pink and yellow) produced till 1945.

1937 – Waterlily produced to 1940. **Apple Blossom** produced to 1940

1939 – Wild Rose

1940 – Foxglove

1943 – **Primula, Poppy**

1945 – Impressed numbers reached 2000

1950+ – By now the post-war stylistic changes had filtered through and the *Leaf* and *Windswept* ranges were in vogue. Motifs included *Hazelnuts, Coffee Beans, Convolvulus, Magnolia, Orchid,* etc. As the decade progressed more 'Contempory' colours, shapes and motifs were introduced. Writing in 1958 the *Pottery Gazette and Glass Trade Review,* while praising *Rouge Royale* as "Probably one of the best known designs for decorative ware ever to come out of the Potteries . . . a favourite for many years all over the world", also spoke highly of innovations like "two-tone leaf ware", the "Hazelnut design" and "Windswept" . . . "Shape, decoration and price have again combined to make this design a best seller throughout the world".

1967 – Impressed marks had reached 2694 (the time of the take-over by Arthur Wood and Son (Longport) plc.

1975 – Introduction of the *Walking Ware* range, designed by Roger Michell and Danka Napiorkowska.

1990 – The **Centenary Vase** produced in a limited edition, just prior to the closure of the factory, by then part of Grosvenor Ceramic Hardware. Few, if any, were sold.

Early Carlton Ware — 1880's vases with gold trim. Silver-plate top and cover.
Courtesy Beverley

Early black and white tableware, hot water jug and teapot.

Another early range was the novelty crested ware, often bought as seaside souvenirs. Many of these items date back to World War I, with aeroplanes, Zepplins and tanks.

Unusual Ginger Jar. Bird of paradise. High lustered background with oil base. Also unusual Ginger Jar and cover **Armond** with butterflies in pale blue background. Foreground shows green **Armond** vase with butterflies. **Armond** is known for butterflies as well as fish. Courtesy Beverley.

Early lustre ware delicately gilded, often with spiders' webs and butterflies. Pattern 3025.

A ginger jar, in a pale green matt glaze in the **Long-tailed Bird** pattern, number 1855.

Souvenir ware decorated with lucky white heather.

Handcraft pair of plates. One with blue and one with black background. Vase with Crinoline Lady with black face. Unusual. Couresty L. Adams.

Unuusal *Handcraft* vase with pale blue background and **Geometric** clouds. Conical Jug, *Handcraft*. Unusual design with thorns and thistles among geometric circles. Courtesy Beverley.

Plum and Orchard vase with Powder bowl with butterflies in *Rouge Royale*.
Courtesy Beverley.

Green Marigold vase with butterfly and green vase with Poppy with two glazes combined, *Handcraft* and enamel. Courtesy L. Adams.

The *Handcraft* **Cherry** pattern.

A **Cherry** bowl and a bowl in the very rare **Crinoline Lady** pattern 3451.

Also rare, pattern 4247, **Shadow Bunny**, on a pair of vases with a **Bluebell Wood** ginger jar.

Small **Geometric** vase in *Rouge Royale* and large red vase with enamel flowers — bluebells. It also comes in green and blue with odd bits in yellow. Courtesy L. Adams.

Early **Geometrics**. Blue vase. Second colourway to *Rouge Royael* vase previously shown. Lightning Flash ginger jar in orange. Seen in green and also in blue. Courtesy L. Adams.

An unusual bookend, pattern 3478 **Hollyhocks**, with a vase in pattern 2655 **Geometric**.

The **Jazz** pattern again, this time on an orange background.

Chinaland on the large green vase, and pattern 2884 a *Chinoiserie* **Egyptian** design on the smaller blue vase.

In the *Handcraft* range, pattern 3694 **Stylised Flowers**.

Humming birds flying in a fairyland setting. Pattern 3281.

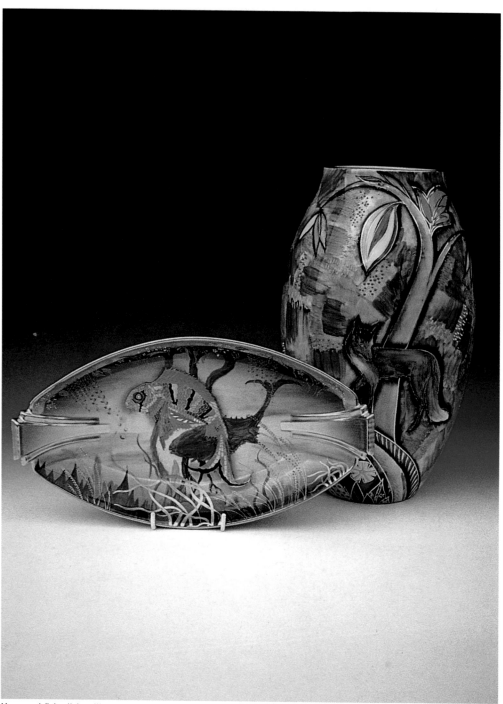

Unusual fish dish with shillouette and fox vase enamel behind. Also Squirrel in this range and fish on page 94. Courtesy L. Adams.

Hollyhocks again, this time on a magnificent ginger jar, with two *Rouge Royale* ginger jars, one with **Humming Birds**, pattern 3281, and another with the **Fantasia** pattern, number 3244.

Fantasia again, this time on a bowl and a biscuit barrel.

Another landscape pattern, 3989 known to collectors as **Tiger Tree.**

Here the exotic **Bird on Waterlily** pattern 3530, is shown on a black background.

. . . and here on the more usual red background, with a wide *Rouge Royale* vase and a ginger jar in the **Jazz** pattern, 3352.

Mestopheles Devil. The mug is *Handcraft* and is unusual in being matt. The jug is high glazed. Courtesy L. Adams.

Here a group of vases are displayed on a chrome and black glass stand incorporating the "Carlton Ware" logo.

Orange background sometimes called **Sunflower Geometric**.

56

The **Egyptian Fan** pattern again, this time turquoise.

Plate, tube-lined unusual with cream background. Courtsey Beverley

A powder-bowl with the **Egyptian Fan** pattern, and a magnificent footed bowl in **Nightingale**.

The interior view of the **Nightingale** bowl.

Early plate with gold trim and high lustered tree. Small plate with Hollyhocks, lustered with matt green background. Courtesy Beverley.

60

More bowls, with (top right) a rare black ground *Cloisonne Ware* jardinère.

Dishes and plaques including the **Egyptian Fan** pattern on a small diamond-shaped dish in the centre, pattern 2975, tube-lined on a matt peach lustre ground plaque in the centre top and a lustre bowl in the **Chinaland** pattern, centre bottom row.

The *Egyptian* design on a large charger, seen here with two vases, pattern 3144 **Black Bird of Paradise** (left) and **Lily of the Valley** (right).

More *Chinoiserie* dishes, one on a cream ground and two smaller *Rouge Royale* items.

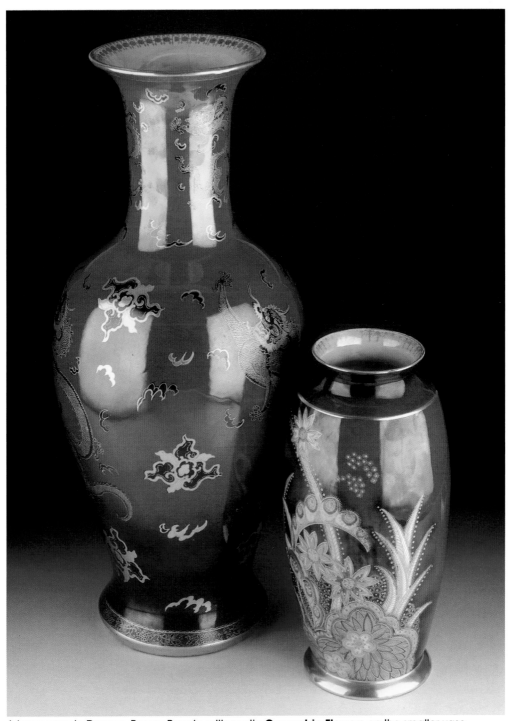

A large vase in **Dragon** *Rouge Royale*, with exotic **Geometric Flowers** on the smaller vase.

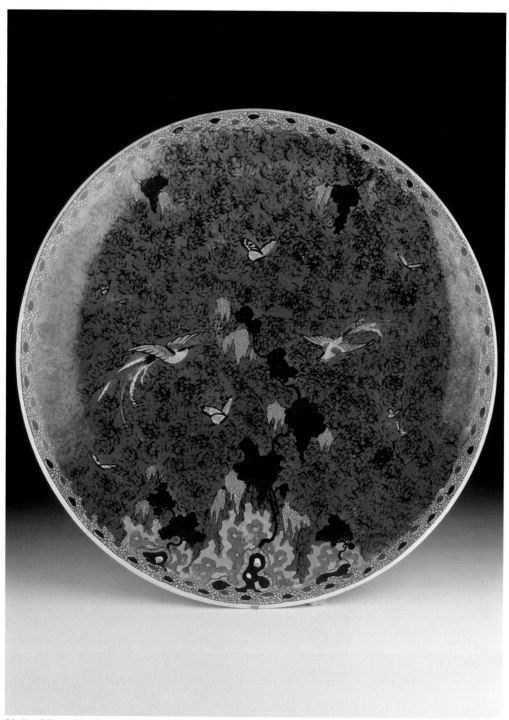

Birds of Paradise fly on this large deep red plaque.

A pair of vases in pattern 3588, with an **Egyptian Fan** vase, pattern 3696, in the centre.

More Oriental scenes decorate the vases shown here, along with exotic birds and stylised flowers. Courtesy Christies.

Pattern 3525 is shown on a vase in the centre with a orange lustre ground, along with blue and white vases from the Handcraft range, and a rare turquoise cyclindrical vase of a **Cavalier and his Lady** in a formal garden. Courtesy Christies.

Tableware, especially spectacular coffee sets, formed a large part of Carlton Ware's output. Pattern 2944 in black, yellow, orange and gilt had silhouetted figures, pattern 3141 a landscape with trees and birds and pattern 3917 combined shades of lemon, pale blue and turquoise on a cream ground in a running pattern. Courtesy Christies.

A sophisticated **Moderne** coffee set in white and gold, with a **Tiger Tree** jug and **Sunburst** ginger jar. Courtesy Christies.

Top row: A green boulster vase decorated with stylised hydrangea blossoms (second left), a Rumidor lustre tobacco jar in pattern 3143 (far right). Centre row: A Tutankhamen ginger jar in powder blue with gilt hieroglyphics (second left), a tall Bleu Royale vase with twisted gilt handles, a footed blue bowl with Persian style flowers, pattern 3050 and an orange footed bowl and stand, pattern 3699 (each end of bottom row), show the wide variety of decorative patterns produced by the factory. Courtesy Christies.

Blue vase with humming-bird and black background vase with Stork.

Bouquets of flowers form the pattern on this large plaque, known as **Sunburst,** number 3387.

Pattern 3525 on a ginger jar with a mottled yellow ground, showing a large Bird of Paradise among flowers.

Carlton copies of Doulton? Verona, Jean and Nan, part of a series that were done in the mid-thirties. Courtesy Beverley.

Guinness advertising range. Toucan Penguin with original shade. Toucan and six small pieces. Small penguin not shown. Seal and Toucan are the only ones done in a large size. Courtesy Beverley

The wide range of Carlton Ware is shown here — a Kien Lung baluster vase, an enamelled jug with an elaborate electroplated mount, three figurines — a woman in evening dress, **Jean** and **New Gloves**, a comical dog, an early novelty footballer cruet and a valuable rare limited edition Conference of Canada commemorative jug. Courtesy Christies.

Another magical bird flies beneath the boughs of a blue willow tree, pattern 4160, while on the smaller dish a squirrel perches on a branch, an extremely rare example of a naturalistic portrayal of an animal.

Biscuit barrel, silver plate top, surrounded by novelty series. Dog part of Pipsqueak and Wilfred series depicted in Daily Mail in 1930s. Cruet set birds, soldier napkin ring, dog with ruffle and Bird cigarette holders. Courtesy of Beverley.

A selection of advertising ware, including a Guinness toucan lamp with the original shade, a rare Guinness penguin lamp-base, a Beefeater Yeoman lamp-base, a Flowers Brewmaster advertising figure, a Guinness musical tankard, "My Grandfather's Clock", a collection of Guinness advertising figures, and some novelty items including Crinoline Lady napkin rings.

A selection of pottery from various factories, including from Carlton Ware three Guinness flying toucans, a balancing seal Guinness lamp-base and a very rare **Mephistopheles** pattern cigarette box.

Three items from Carlton Ware's popular *Salad Ware* range, many still in use today.

Carlton Ware produced many novelty items based on playing card motifs — bridge parties and whist drives were popular pastimes of the day. Here a cruet is made up from the four suits of cards, while a later cruet takes the form of colourful shells.

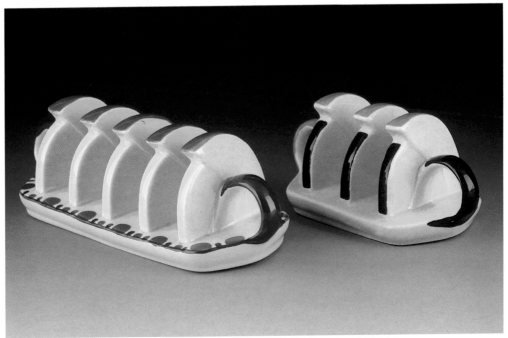

Toast-racks were also intended to add a touch of colour to the breakfast table.

Jug in Liberty Stripe and Sandwich Set. Courtesy Beverley.

The *Anemone* range was similarly vivid, with a high glaze and strong colours.

The first of Carlton Ware's naturalistic patterns, **Oak Tree**, has been popular from the early thirties and is still a favourite today.

Garden Wall was matt glazed, in beige or pale blue, moulded with brick-work and a scattering of cottage flowers.

The *Fruit Basket* range was highly glazed and come in many table-ware shapes as well as bowls and dishes.

The *Oak Tree* or *Acorn* range was matt glazed, but came in strong, bold shapes, either on a beige ground for **Day,** or on a grey-blue ground for **Night**.

Some of the more ornamental lines were lightly touched with gilt.

By the mid-thirties, Carlton Ware had begun making their floral embossed ranges, leaves forming the shape and a spray of blossom the decoration *Apple Blossom* was a very popular range.

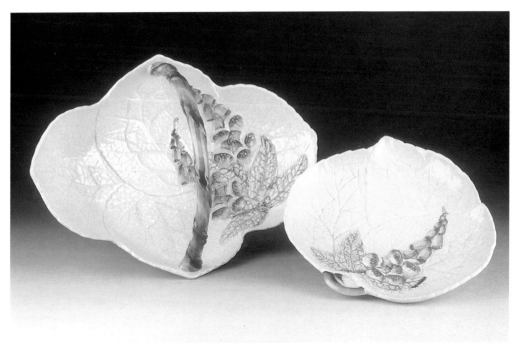

Foxglove too came in a wide range of shapes and sizes

In other ranges, like *Pink Buttercup,* the flower itself formed the whole of the shape, as in this rare cheese-dish.

Green vase with lightning tree. Matt finish with high glaze trees. Bowl with **Geometric** flash flowers, pattern both internal and external. Courtesy Beverley.

Toast-racks, cruets and egg-cups were all made in the floral ranges.

Larger items too, like the teapots, were very decorative. Here a teapot is trimmed with a buttercup garland while the other is in the *Waterlily* range.

Cups and saucers were made to complete the tableware sets, like this in **Wild Rose** (or **Dog Rose**), with two **Buttercup** examples.

Hydrangea seen here in its two colourways, is a particularly collectable pattern.

Some tiny jam or butter dishes came boxed, with a ceramic knife or spoon, seen here in the **Primula** pattern. The *Springtime* dish has a "basket-weave" handle.

Berries also made a decorative motif, including blackberries and raspberries with their leaves.

More elaborate floral patterns were achieved by the "print and enamel" method, with touches of gilding.

Assorted enamel glazed and lustre coffee sets. Courtesy Christies.

Elegant dishes like these were made in a smooth finish (apple green) or in the watered silk effect (pink cream). As war was imminent items like these may have been intended for export.

At home or abroad, *Rouge Royale* never lost its popularity.

After the war, tastes had changed and strong, bold two-tone colours and windswept shapes became popular.

Fruit shapes were still popular, but they were vivid, bold colours and slick outlines, contrasting with the earlier blackberry jampot here and the naturalistic strawberry cruet.

Floral items like these from the *Magnolia* range were made in modern colours with contrasting lids.

The *Hazelnut* range was very successful and so was *Convolvulus,* again in sweeping contemporary lines.

One of Carlton Ware's greatest novelty successes was the *Walking Ware* teaset, made during the time the factory was part of the Arthur Wood organisation

Walking Ware remained popular for many years, and has recently been reissued by the Price-Kensington factory. Teapots, too, continued to be made under the Carlton Ware name right up to its final years. Here the Red Baron flies again!

Two **Chinaland** vases, number 2728.

Early claret jug with silver plate mount.

Lustre fish vase (see page 50).

Handcraft series **Green Flash** pattern 3387, c1928.

Top row: lustre Persian Temple vase, orange marigold vase. Bottom Row: *Rouge Royale* ginger jar with flying ducks, pale blue lustre vase with butterflies. Courtesy Christies.

A Toby Jug cruet set.

Lustre Tiger Tree with enamel.

STARTING A CARLTON WARE COLLECTION

With Carlton Ware, it is unusual for a collector to buy 'across the board', building up a collection which is a mixture of all the various Carlton Ware ranges, though of course there is no reason why this should not be done.

Probably the most successful way to do it would be to treat each section of the collection as a mini-collection, some ranges being more suited to specific parts of the house than others. Advertising ware, say, for the kitchen, lustre ware for the sitting-room and tableware for the dining-room.

Generally, however, a collector will decide to collect one particular type of Carlton Ware and this choice will depend, apart from personal preference, upon the funds available and the space where the pottery will be housed.

A collection of lustre ware items will obviously be much more costly than one of novelty cruets or floral embossed ware. Safety precautions in the matter of display will need to be greater, as a single item smashed or damaged will represent a much greater loss. This is not to lose sight of the fact that one of the most refreshing aspects of collecting is that as much satisfaction can be gained from a collection of modest financial cost as from one in which a small fortune has been invested – it is the enjoyment of collecting which counts, not the monetary outlay.

Even within the parameters set by the collector, further choices will need to be made. For instance, a collection of floral embossed ware may, in itself, be 'across the board', covering all shapes and patterns, or it may be restricted to a favourite pattern or group of patterns, perhaps all being chosen with a matching background colour, say yellow or green.

Sometimes shape may be the deciding factor, for instance the popular leaf-shaped dish, which may be displayed flat, propped up on a small plate-stand or wall-hung, gives a wide choice of options.

With lustre ware, single examples can be so striking they are sufficient alone, but here, too, a collector may have a favourite pattern and aim at getting it on the full range of shapes.

Equally, a collection of plaques and wall-plates in all the available patterns will look very effective and be simple to display, though obviously representing a large outlay.

A compromise might be to collect two Carlton Ware ranges, simultaneously, one of formal vases and plaques added to gradually as funds permit, and a novelty collection of inexpensive pieces – cruets, perhaps, or salad ware – to be built up by impulse buys.

Post-war Carlton Ware remains relatively inexpensive compared with the rarer pre-war items, so this method could also be used here, the pieces from each period being shown in separate displays, one being fairly modern in style, the other with more of a period charm.

An additional advantage would be that it is still sometimes possible to find post-war Carlton Ware pieces sold at very modest prices, perhaps in charity shops or at bric a brac sales or flea markets. Since these ranges, for example the Windswept shapes and the Two-tone colourways reflect the design ideas of their own day, they are likely to be very sought after as the post-war decade comes into collecting fashion.

As with most other potteries, coffee cans can be very effective as a group, and can be displayed in a limited space. Toastracks are similarly popular, and, particularly with Carlton Ware, cruets.

Since the Carlton Ware factory produced such a vast range of patterns, it is usually possible to choose items to harmonise with any colour scheme, and this will obviously be taken into consideration when making collecting choices.

Almost any items will fit into a modern or traditional interior. They display well on polished surfaces, stripped pine or white or cream gloss shelving as well as on glass shelves or in glass-fronted cabinets.

Gradually it is quite likely that the collection will by means of purchases or gifts outgrow its space and as the collector becomes more knowledgeable there will be pieces it seems appropriate to discard. At this point it may well be possible, by taking an occasional stall at an antique or Art Deco fair, to off-load items surplus to requirements and incidentally raise cash for further, more desirable purchases.

This is an aspect of collecting which may develop into a lucrative spare-time hobby or even in later life into a full-time retirement occupation.

As collecting becomes an absorbing hobby, it will in any case usually begin to take up more spare time, as fairs both locally and far away will be visited, and holiday venues will provide new contacts to be followed up.

As Carlton Ware becomes increasingly popular with collectors, it is featuring more frequently in articles in antiques magazines and journals about interior design. These, collected together in a folder with transparent display sleeves will make a fascinating scrapbook of photographs and information which will add interest and enjoyment to the collection and provide useful reference material to assist dating and pattern identification. Collectors are often alerted by friends when these articles appear and it is always worthwhile to check up on these references as even if not concerned with the range being collected, they may include data about the factory itself.

RECORD KEEPING

Record keeping is important because as the collection grows a vast amount of detailed information needs storing and to rely on memory alone is unwise and ineffective.

It is best to begin right at the start with accurate notes regarding each item, its provenance, shape, pattern, date of purchase, condition and cost, as well as where and when it was bought. Most dealers will give receipts if required and this is advisable.

If a price lower than the initial asking price has been agreed with the seller, a note should be made of the original price as well as the price actually paid.

Polaroid photographs are invaluable for identification in case of theft. Individual marks such as minor firing flaws or faulty brushwork should be noted as these distinguish an item from the collection from ones which otherwise appear identical.

Details on the base should also be noted either by description or photograph.

The value of keeping records will be proved when the time inevitably comes when some of the items are to be sold, either because they no longer fit in with the direction the collection is taking or because a special purchase makes the raising of additional funds imperative. With the backing of detailed records the collector can approach a dealer with more confidence and the selling or part-exchanging of items is likely to be more satisfactory to all concerned.

Though there may never be any intention of selling items on or of moving across into dealing, the fact remains that although the collection will, by its fascination and decorative qualities, more than repay the cumulative financial investment involved, it is nevertheless interesting and reassuring to monitor the rising prices being asked for Cartlton Ware, particularly as it appears with increasing frequency in the major auction rooms, and as ranges at present less eagerly sought begin to be of interest to collectors, you should note the higher prices being asked for them in consequence of the rising demand.

INSURANCE

Inevitably a collection will eventually need separate insurance as its increasing value will be too great to be covered within the normal household insurance.

Whether the collection consists of a few highly-priced large items of lustre ware or a vast array of smaller pieces in less expensive ranges, it is best to consult a reputable insurance company with a view to discovering the most suitable policy to cover for both theft and damage. Regular, probably annual, updating will be needed as the collection is added to and also prices rise, thus increasing the total insured value of the collection.

The cost of insurance will be proportionate to the total value of the insured items, though precautions that have been taken against burglary will help to keep premiums down, as with ordinary household insurance.

However, because of the fragile nature of pottery, it is unlikely that in the course of a routine burglary the collection would be recognised as being worth taking since easily sold household equipment would be the object of the exercise. Unfortunately, though, the possibility exists that knowledgeable thieves might target a known collector and it is wise to avoid being too specific about the exact addrerss and size of the collection.

Much more likely to be a hazard is accidental damage in the course of re-arrangement of items, dusting or the visits of children or pets, and making a claim that can be backed up by "before" and "after" photographs is much easier than if no record exists of what the broken items looked like in their original state, This is, indeed usually required, and some insurance companies ask for two independent statements, from reputable antique dealers, to verify the value of the broken pottery as claimed by the collector.

Of paramount importance if the collection includes, say, a complete and expensive coffee set, or even a rare novelty cruet or two, is the factor of 'parts or sets', since unless specifically arranged, the insurance may not cover the total value of the set even though the destruction of one item may be disastrous if it is irreplacable. This must be borne in mind since the replacement value of a single coffee cup or a pepper-pot bears no relation to the cost of replacing a whole set or a complete cruet.

If it proves impossible to replace a particular rare item that has been damaged, restoration may be the only alternative and this will probably be covered by the insurance company provided prior estimates for the work are submitted. Since restoration, depending, of course on its extent, can be considered to reduce the value of an item by around one third of its perfect price, this reduction should be included in the cost of the claim along with the estimate for restoration.

RESTORATION

The three main considerations in buying pottery are pattern, shape and condition, and of the three condition is perhaps the most important, since poor condition can spoil the appearance of a superb pattern or an unusual shape, even if the item is extremely rare and otherwise very desirable.

Restoration of a piece to the equivalent of its original state either by repairing damage to the body or deterioration of the paintwork can, by a highly-skilled restorer, be carried out so expertly that it is virtually undetectable. However, the fact remains that the piece is restored and so is reduced in value by a considerable amount. No reputable dealer would attempt to pass it off as a perfect piece and charge full price for it.

Very minor damage, say, a hairline crack at the back of a piece may be acceptable to a collector when the piece is being bought solely for its visual beauty which is not impaired when carefully placed so that the crack does not show. In such a case there seems little point in going to the trouble and expense of restoration. One of the dangers of collecting is getting obsessive and fanatical, and it is as well to be aware of this. Collecting is primarily intended for pleasure, after all.

On the other hand, the restoration of a piece which otherwise might be at some point thrown away can be regarded as a form of conservation, so this must be taken into consideration. It goes without saying that a damaged item will be sold at a price reflecting its far from perfect state, thus allowing at least in part for the cost of restoration.

If restoration is decided upon, it is worth taking trouble to find out the name of a restorer who is known to be an expert. Tact is needed, since dealers may resent enquiries on this point as being a reflection on their stock. In the first instance, the local museum might be able to help, or other collectors could perhaps advise.

Modern restoration methods improve all the time and this is why trust is an important element in buying and selling pottery. Generally speaking, dealers are well aware that their reputation is of greater value than a quick profit, and point out damage or restoration as a matter of course. Then the decision rests with the purchaser as to whether or not to accept the piece. A chip on the back of a plate that is going to hang on the wall hardly matters to one collector while another will feel it is unacceptable. But there is all the difference in the world between buying something as perfect and finding later it is flawed, and most dealers will willingly take back an item which has proved not as thought at the time of purchase – though always with the proviso that the damage has not occured after the time of sale.

Usually, lustre ware, having been from the first a luxury range, has been well looked after and is unlikely to bear the marks of careless handling or surface wear. The occasional hairline crack or a minor chip on items of such superior quality would probably justify the cost of restoration. Items from other ranges, however, may turn up damaged and since they are in much greater supply it probably makes sense to wait for a perfect item rather than go to the trouble and expense of having damaged ones restored.

Some minor restoration may be carried out at home. Staining inside a tea or coffe-pot often yields to an overnight soaking with a solution of mild detergent or bicarbonate of soda, while gentle washing removes surface grime, inaccessible corners being carefully cleaned with a soft toothbrush.

Crazing is a vexed question. The surface glaze on a piece inevitably tends to crack over the years, but the extent to which this happens varies from piece to piece. Heavy crazing inevitably detracts from the appearance of an item, so except in very rare cases it is probably best to wait for a less crazed example.Minor crazing, however, will be acceptable to most collectors.

LIGHTING AND DISPLAY

Lighting is important to enhance any collection and this is particularly true of Carlton Ware as the high glazes are shown off to their best advantage by being well lit. This is especially true of the lustre ware range.

Where a china cabinet of the period will fit in with existing furniture, this will house at least part of the collection and sometimes will have built-in lighting of its own, which must be re-wired if the original wiring is still in position, as it will not conform to modern safety standards. If no lightning exists, it is a simple matter to add lighting to the interior. Modern display cabinets will also suit Carlton Ware ranges, as will glass shelves in an alcove, when lighting from the top or the bottom will shine right through the display. If sliding glass doors can be added, this cuts down on dusting and the risk of damage.

As well as the obviously wall-hung items like plaques and plates, many of the pieces in the floral embossed range are suitable for hanging, and a range of plate-hangers in all sizes is obtainable from most iron-mongers, the only proviso being that plastic-covered hooks are essential to protect the rim of the items where the hanger grips it.

Generally speaking, groups of items from the same range harmonise best together, some collectors preferring to group pieces of only one pattern in a display, but this is a matter of personal choice. Many floral patterns mix well, if there is an overall background colour.

Tableware displays go well on a dresser or in glass-fronted kitchen cabinets.

Where there is any fear of items being dislodged, say on a plate-rail round a room or on a window-sill, a piece of Blu-tack positioned out of sight will help give stability. Be careful not to put Blu-tack or sticky tape on gold enamel. Gold is fired on top of the glaze at a low temperature and can come off with harsh treatment.

Spot-lighting can be used to emphasize larger pieces where they may have been chosen to point up the colour-scheme of a room.

Small items like cruets, ash-trays and toastracks group best together and require a space where their small component parts are out of danger.

Advertising ware looks well lit by one of the several attractive matching lamps that are available. Again, re-wiring is essential if not already carried out.

Sometimes it is possible to buy display aids issued by the factory to their retailers and when these are available they make an attractive addition to a Carlton Ware display. These may take the form of ceramic plaques or even metal units supporting glass shelves and incorporating the Carlton Ware logo. (See Christie's, South Kensington's catalogue 27/8/92 Lot 378).

RARITY

The luxury ranges, like lustre ware and the matt-glazed Handcraft ware, being made in less quantity, still tend today to be rarer than those intended for everyday use like the floral embossed ware, made in much greater quanity.

However, being decorative as well as useful, the floral embossed ware was frequently used only for display, and this has tended to preserve it in good condition.

Items which have attracted damage are generally teapots, coffee pots and jugs, where spouts, lids and handles need to be carefully checked. Lids on ginger-jars or pot pourri holders have often been broken and if missing seriously affect the value of the item.

One particularly accident-prone item is the floral embossed lidded chocolate cup or mug, the attractive lid often having fallen victim to an accident, and this makes a complete example particularly valuable.

Some items are attractive to other collectors apart from Carlton Ware collectors. These include cruets, toastracks, commemorative items, advertising items, nursery ware, ceramic napkin rings and coffee cans.

Inevitably items more recently made are available in much greater quanitity, and post-war shapes and patterns are more easily found than pre-war ones, so it is probably worthwhile to collect some good examples of these before prices rise any higher.

Particularly collectable are items which have motifs based on the Egyptian excavations of 1922, a large ginger-jar, for example, reaching nearly £2000 at auction in 1993.

Sets of floral embossed ware, such as the Tea For Two sets, cost more bought as a set than if the items were bought individually. If attemping to match items to a set, it is important to bear in mind that the backstamps should match if possible.

Some patterns seem to come into fashion and for a time, at least, command very high prices, Pink Buttercup for example fetching much more than the same items in Yellow Buttercup. In general it seems wise to avoid getting caught up in trends and to choose items for their suitability for the collection rather than for their current fashion appeal.

AVAILABILITY

Obviously the availability of the Carlton Ware range you want will depend on how much was made initially and how far it has survived the passage of the years.

Most collectors would agree that a few good pieces are better than a miscellaneous collection of items which do not cohere as a group.

It is best to get at least a working knowledge of Carlton Ware ranges before beginning to buy pieces. This avoids costly mistakes.

Most areas now have dealers either with shops of their own or stalls in antique centres selling Art Deco pottery. Even ten years ago, this was not the case. Among these dealers, some may have a particular bias towards Carlton Ware, and they will probably be willing to look out for special items or even give 'first refusal' on pieces which come their way.

Through these dealers and other collectors locally, it will be possible to get to know about Carlton Ware dealers further afield. They will also have knowledge about fairs, some general fairs with a proporation of stalls selling Art Deco, and some specialist Art Deco fairs of which there are now an increasing number.

Local events like school bazaars and charity fund-raising events often have bric-a-brac stalls which may repay a visit, since they may have Carlton Ware pieces for sale at very low prices. If these are in good condition it is worth offering a higher price so that next time they will make contact before the event if more good pieces surface. Charity shops are similarly worth cultivating, as they are glad to have regular and generous customers. These sources are, however, more likely to yield post-war rather than pre-war items.

Advertising in antiques magazines sometimes brings good results provided the advertisement makes clear which Carlton Ware ranges are of interest.

Magazines also carry details of fairs and auctions, though the best source of information is naturally the trade press. The weekly Antiques Trade Gazette is sold on subscription only, as is Antiques Bulletin, though this is available at some fairs. Antiques Today is monthly and is also sold on subscription as well as being available in antiques shops, markets and fairs.

Auctions are also useful since the prices paid can be a good guide to current trends, unless there is particular competition for a rare piece which gives rise to a freak high price.

Auction houses locally and in London can be useful as a source of collectable items, too. Dealers after all have their overheads and profit margins to consider so are likely to be more cautious in their bids than private collectors, who only have to bear the buyer's premium in mind.

For collectors who cannot attend auctions personally it is worth getting to know a porter who will bid according to instructions in return for a modest tip if successful.

Particularly in the case of London auction houses like Christie's South Kensington who produce high-quality catalogues with ample illustrations, it is worth obtaining a catalogue and pricing it up after the sale from the list of results which can be obtained, making a useful, up-to-date price-guide.

FAKES AND REPRODUCTIONS

Carlton Ware is so popular that modern versions of early items, for example, the sets of flying toucans, have been produced, but whether these are regarded as fakes or acceptable reproductions is up to the individual collector. It seems that the original moulds have been kept and used more recently, but even if this is the case, they should certainly not be offered at the price appropriate to early original items.

Some floral embossed ware has been issued quite legitimately with a later backstamp, and provided no attempt is made to pass this off as being from the factory's pre-war days this seems acceptable. They, too, are made from the original moulds, though they are not made by the original owners. The colours are sometimes not exactly right and the definition of the low relief is sometimes blurred by repeated use of the mould. Apart from a large, clearly marked Centenary Vase in lustre ware and some ranges of *Rouge Royale* also carrying a recognisably later stamp, issued while the name was being used by Grosvenor Ceramic Hardware Ltd, it seems unlikely that fakes will occur in the lustre range as the costs of making these would be prohibitive.

Some novelty ware and novelty teapots were issued by Grosvenor Ceramic Hardware Ltd. but again these items carried the tiny script mark which the firm used immediately prior to the final demise of the Carlton Ware name. They are Carlton Ware items but not yet collectable, though they may be one day. From the days when Carlton Ware Ltd. was taken over by Arthur Wood and Sons, in 1967, many novelty mugs, jugs, teapots, toastracks and cruets were made and most collectors would include these without question in the appropriate sections of their collections. They are also sought after by collectors of novelty teapots, toastracks, cruets etc. so are not easy to find.

Probably the safest way to avoid the inclusion of dubious material is to concentrate on the inter-war years and buy as far as possible from reputable dealers. This avoids the danger, too, of restored goods being passed off as perfect. At all times the best advice is not to buy if there is any reason for feeling at all doubtful.

Already reproductions have become currently accepted (though not by all collectors!) of Clarice Cliff items, and some Susie Cooper sets were re-issued at the time of the 1987 exhibition, so good quality Carlton Ware reproductions may be made which are acceptable to most collectors. While authentic Carlton Ware pieces remain available in sufficient quantity it seems unlikely they would find favour with serious collectors but it is a matter which each collector must resolve when and if the situation arises. Fakes, that is, items intended to deceive, obviously are never acceptable at any time.

ANTIQUE MARKETS, SPECIALIST SHOPS AND FAIRS

Alfie's Antique Market, 13/25 Church Street, London, NW8 (Various dealers)

Antiquarius, 235 King's Road, London, SW3

Antiques on the Square, 2 Sandford Court, Sandford Avenue, Church Stretton, Shropshire (Chris Radford)

Chenil Galleries, 181 King's Road, London, SW3 (various dealers)

Gray's Antique Market, 58 Davies Street. London W1 (various dealers)

Stratford-upon Avon – Stratford Antique Centre, Ely Street, Shop Unit 4 in the Courtyard – Art Deco Ceramics (Howard & Pat Watson)

Beverley, 30 Church Street, London NW8

Bizarre Decorative Arts, (Malcolm Lamb) 116 Manchester Road,

Altrincham, Cheshire, WA14 4PY

Chrome (Keith & Carol Upton), 23 The Shambles, York, YO1 2LZ. (0904 631960)

Nantwich Art Deco and Decorative Arts (Michael Poole and Peter Savill), 87 Welsh Row, Nantwich, Cheshire CW5 5ET

Alexandra Palace Fair, Wood Green, London N22 (700 stalls, many selling Carlton Ware)

Sandown Park, Esher, Surrey (afternoon and evening fair)

Midlands Art Deco Fair, Hilton National Hotel, Warwick

National Art Deco Fair, Loughborough Town Hall, Loughborough

South of England Art Deco Fair, Brighton Centre, Brighton

Kensington Decorative Arts Fair, Kensington Town Hall, London

AUCTION TRENDS

In keeping with the growing trend across the country, most London auction houses now include Carlton Ware in their sales of Twentieth Century Decorative Arts, and though generally these are high quality items mainly from the lustre ware and Handcraft ranges, figurines and floral embossed ware as well as advertising items are sometimes included, especially sets of items like Tea for Two sets or Early Morning sets.

Post-war items are seldom included, though, in the 27/8/92 specialist sale at Christie's South Kensington (Doulton Ware in the morning, Poole Pottery in the early afternoon and Carlton Ware at 3.00 p.m.) besides the spectacular array of very expensive items was a Convolvulus Tea for Two which fetched £60.

Walking Ware items were also included as was a Blush Ware biscuit barrel pattern 1846, showing the wide time-scale of items now sought by collectors.

Salad Ware was also included and it is worth noting that Salad Ware is now being collected 'across the board'; collections being formed which include Carlton Ware items, pieces by Crown Devon and also Beswick items. Lobster and Tomato Ware also appeared again at the second Christie's Carlton Ware auction (23/8/93) and fetched good prices, while a 'large collection' of 1960s and 1970s tableware fetched £99.

It was, however, noticeable that the highest prices at the first auction went for pieces with a strong Egyptianesque influence, though ginger jars in all patterns were popular and a particularly exotic coffee set went for £650. At the second sale, ginger jars and coffee sets remained popular, though the highest prices this time were obtained for items with what might be called 'storybook' decoration – Pattern 3769 (Mephistopheles), Pattern 3332 (a dragon attacking bats) and Pattern 3595 (a dragon confronting a traveller). Perhaps this indicates that the vogue for 'Swords and Sorcery' fiction and computer games is now having its effect on the world of antiques and collectables!

The increasing interest in Carlton Ware is also reflected in the proliferation of articles not only in magazines for collectors but also in journals of interior design which stress the decorative quality of all the Carlton Ware ranges.

PRICE AND RARITY GUIDE

With such an enormous range of items, it is difficult to suggest with any accuracy what it will cost to collect Carlton Ware. Price will depend largely on rarity and how keen the collector is to acquire the piece under consideration. One important factor is that both the buyer and seller should feel the transaction to be fair, since otherwise there will not be a basis for an on-going relationship. Trust is an essential part of collecting and that will be lost if the bargain is struck too hard by either party to the transaction. Many transient factors can have a passing effect on prices – media attention, an auction with head-line hitting results, even rumours on the Stock Exchange causing unease in the country at large. Also, overheads vary from place to place and inevitably there are times when a dealer will feel it prudent to take a smaller, quicker profit rather than wait for a more affluent customer. Being in the right place at the right time makes a lot of difference.

That said, there are a few general guidelines which may be helpful, provided it is borne in mind that they are not hard and fast rules. What follows assumes very good condition throughout and where appropriate indicates price ranges for (1) patterns made in quantity and therefore easy to find, (2) patterns produced in lesser amounts and therefore rarer, and finally (3) those patterns which are particularly sought by collectors either because they are very rare or because they have been applied to a rare shape or both, for instance a cheesedish in Pink Buttercup or a Mephistopheles ginger jar, pattern 3769, in which case the price would certainly break all records!

Carlton Ware is also a developing subject with much more yet to be discovered. As popularity increases, which is likely, then so too will prices. Please use this guide as a very general indicator wihic is only as correct as a changing market will allow. If it helps you decide whether a piece is worth around £5, £50 or £500 it will have served its purpose.

Advertising Ware
Note: This is an area where modern replicas are being offered for sale. This should be reflected in a low price and frankness on the part of the seller. If a price appropriate to an original 1930s item is being asked and any doubt exists, don't buy.
Sets of three flying toucans: £150-£200/$225-$300
Toucan lamp, original paper shade: £150-£250/$225-$375
Toucan lamp, original plastic shade: £100-£150/$150/$225
Seal lamp, balancing globe: £200-£250/$300-$375
Penguin lampbase (rare): £250-£300/$375-$450

Guinness musical tankard, Bass musical tankard: £125-£175/$185-$260
Guinness figures – keeper, kangaroo, ostrich, seal etc: £65-£85/$95-$125
Advertising figures (according to size, rarity): £80-£200/$120-$300
Tankards, jugs, ash-trays, match-holders: £15-£50/$22-$75

Crested and Commemorative Ware

Rarity here is the main deciding factor, age also being a deciding factor with commemorative ware, fragility with crested ware, since guns, propeller etc. were easily broken.

Crested

Small items – vases, jugs, ewers, etc: under £10/$15.
Novelty items – stick telephone, flat iron, grandfather clocks, etc: £15-£25/$22-$35
World War One items – tank, ship, gun, soldier: £35-£150/$50-$225+
Buildings – lighthouses, cottages, war memorial: £40-£100/$60-$150+
Animals and people – £20-£120/$30-$180

Commemorative

Events (exhibitions, etc.): £15-£45/$22-$67
Royal occasions – tankards, mugs, cups and saucers: £15-£50/$22-$75
Plates: £35-£150/$47-$225

Novelty Items

Cruets -Bass player set: around £45/$67
Figurines: £150-£250/$225-375
Footballer set: £100-£200/$150-$300 according to condition
Crinoline lady: £75-£125/$105-185
Novelty dogs: £35-£55/$50-$80+
Napkin rings – Crinoline ladies, servant girls etc. £35-£45/$50-67 each.

Post-war Items

At present these remain less collected than pre-war Carlton Ware and so the price depends on the venue and pieces turning up. Younger collectors could find this period, therefore, a very fruitful field as prices are sure to rise over the years and what can be bought very reasonably now will probably prove an excellent investment as time goes by. Items now are usually well under £10/$15 for two-tone, Windswept and Leaf items, though obviously Walking Ware and novelty teapots fetch higher prices as they have a wider appeal.

Blush Ware

These early products of the Carlton Ware factory combine well with other late Victorian pottery by Royal Worcester, Crown Devon and Minton, with their delicate sprays of flowers and gilded swags, so they appeal to collectors of the period rather than the pottery itself. Prices, therefore, depend on shape rather than pattern, items with fragile elements like handles and knobs being more expensive, while metalwork must be in pristine condition. Some items such as plates and simple dishes will be around £50-£80/$75-$120, while comports, cheese dishes, biscuit barrels, bowls and urns will fetch between £100-£150/$150-$225.

Lustre Ware and Handcraft

Group 1 – Chinoiserie (gilt only), early formal floral sprays, early plain lustre and realistic floral patterns.

Group 2 – Silhouette and stylised floral, early lustre with gilt decoration, Chinoiserie (gilt and enamels). Most bird/fantasy landscapes, Chinaland (3015) Crinoline lady (3451), Hollyhocks (3478).

Group 3 – Tutenkhamen (2710) Egyptian Fan (3696) Jazz (3252), Sunburst (3387) Bird of Paradise (3525), Geometric (2655), Chinese Carp (0000) and other exotic fish eg (3971). Nightingale and other elaborate patterns.

Vases (height)	Group 1	Group 2	Group 3
Small 10-15 cm.	£60–£80/$90-$120	£80–£150/$120-$225	£150–£250/$225-$325
Medium 15-25 cm.	£90–£120/$135-$180	£120–£200/$180-$300	£200–£350/$300-$525
Large 30-36 cm.	£130–£180/$195-$270	£200–£400/$300-$600	£400–£850/$600-$1275

Bowls (width)			
15-20cm	£40–£80/$60-$120	£80–£120/$120-$180	£120–£200/$180-$300
20-25cm	£80–£120/$120-$180	£120–£170/$180-$250	£170–£250/$250-$325
28-36cm	£120–£170/$180-$250	£200–£350/$300-$525	£250–£500/$325-$750

Ginger Jars			
Medium	£120–£150/$180-$225	£200–£300/$300-$450	£300–£450/$450-$675
Large	£200–£300/$300-$450	£300–£450/$450-$675	£400–£900/$600-$1350

(Exceptional auction result – £1900/$2850 for Pattern 2710, 27/8/92)

Plaques & Chargers			
Medium	£120–£150/$180-$225	£200–£250/$300-$325	£250–£350/$325-$525
Large	£170–£220/$250-$330	£220–£300/$330-$450	£300–£450/$450-$675
Coffee Sets	£150–£250/$225-$325	£250–£350/$325-$525	£350–£600/$525-$900

(Exceptional auction result – £650/$975 for Pattern 3406, Melon, 27/8/92)

Biscuit Barrels	£100–£150/$150-$225	£120–£170/$180-$250	£170–£250/$250-$325

Novelties

Cigarette boxes, inkstands, powder
bowls, etc)   £50–£100/$75-$150   £100–£150/$150-$225   £150–£200/$225-$300
(Exceptional auction result – £390/$585 for cigarette box, Pattern 3692, 27/8/92)

Floral Embossed Ware

Group 1 – Apple Blossom, Foxglove, Primula, Wild Rose, etc.

Group 2 – Waterlily, Yellow Buttercup, Blackberry, Fruit Basket, Springtime, Oak Tree, Garden Wall, etc.

Group 3 – Pink Buttercup, Hydrangea, Poppy, etc.

Dishes	Group 1	Group 2	Group 3
(leaf or flower shape)			
13 cm.	£15–£20/$22-$40	£20–£25/$30-$35	£20–£30/$30-$45
18 cm.	£20–£30/$30-$45	£25–£35/$35-$55	£30–£40/$45-$60
23 cm.	£30–£35/$45-$55	£35–£40/$55-$60	£40–£50/$60-$75
Bowls			
Oval	£40–£50/$60-$75	£55–£65/$80-$95	£60–£75/$90-$110
(sometimes 2 flowers)			
Teapots	£65–£85/$95-$125	£80–£120/$120-$180	£120–£150/$180-$225
Preserve pots	£35–£45/$45-$67	£40–£55/$60-$85	£55–£85/$85-$125
Boxed sets			
(tiny dishand knife			
or spoon)	£25–£35/$35-$55	£35–£50/$55-$75	£50–£80/$75-$120

Early Morning Sets (or "Tea for Two")
incl. teapot, milk jug, sugar basin,
2 cups and saucers,

	Group 1	Group 2	Group 3
1 biscuit plate:	£100–£250/$150-$375	£150–£250/$225-375	£200–£350/$400-$525

Toastracks, cruets, other

	Group 1	Group 2	Group 3
smaller items:	£25–£35/$35-$55	£35–£55/$55-$85	£55–£85/$85-$125

A CARLTON WARE CHRONOLOGY

c1890   James Frederick Wiltshaw, J.A.Robinson and H.T. Robinson set up in business at the Carlton Works, Stoke on Trent. Ribbon mark with W & R centrally placed, plus Stoke on Trent, swallow above.

1893   The firm was first registered in Stoke on Trent.

1894   Carlton Ware became the factory's trade name, the trade-mark being a circular disc with W & R Stoke on Trent round the edge, a swallow in the centre, a crown above and Carlton Ware below. Blush Ware, lustre items and traditional tableware in production.

1906   China production began, the trade-mark being as above but with the word "China" replacing "Ware".

1911   The partnership was dissolved, James Wiltshaw becoming sole proprietor. Crested souvenir ware and commemorative items were popular, especially patriotic subjects during World War 1.

1918   James Frederick Wiltshaw (1861-1918) died in tragic railway accident. His son Frederick Cuthbert Wiltshaw, a former flying ace, took over.

1920   By now the firm was well-known for lustre decoration in a range of 12 colours.

1922   Discovery of the tomb of Tutenkhamen led to Egyptian style decoration becoming popular. A range of lustre items with Egyptian motifs was developed by Carlton Ware, notably some designed by Horace A Wain.

1925   Exhibition des Arts Decoratifs in Paris led to the use of Art Deco motifs by Carlton Ware, including spectacular designs by Enoch Boulton.

1926   Novelty earthenware and salad ware introduced.

c1927   New trademark introduced - Carlton Ware in script. Made in England below and Trade Mark below that, in use to the mid-thirties. Script mark of Carlton China Made in England also used, till the mid Fifties.

c1928   Birks, Rawlins & Co., Vine Street, Stoke on Trent, taken over to allow for expansion of china production, including dainty teasets in patterns like Springtime and Delphininium.

1929   Oven-to-tableware introduced. Handcraft range also now in production.

c1930   "Fruit Basket" pattern introduced. Advertising ranges launched.

1934   Oak Tree range began, the impressed mark now around 1098.

1935   The Garden Wall range began, the impressed mark now being around 1238. Mr. W.G. Purser, a chartered account, joined the company, later becoming Manager Director. A new, smaller script mark was introduced, with Made in England, Trade Mark, Registered

Australian Design (plus sometimes also Registered Applied For) and used till the mid-Forties. (The Australian reference was to prevent copying of export ware.)

1936 Floral and fruit embossed ware introduced. Buttercup, yellow and pink (until 1945) began. Impressed number 1395 (a small Jam dish and knife) intermittently to 2046. By October pattern numbers had reached 1411.

1937 Waterlily (Shape numbers intermittent between 1590 and 1902) Apple Blossom (Shape numbers intermittent between 1614-2008).

1939 Wild Rose. By May pattern numbers had reached 1734. The outbreak of war led to many restrictions on decorated ware, much being restricted to export.

1940 Foxglove. (Impressed mark no. 1870 onwards).

1943 Primula, Poppy,

1945 By the end of the war, shape numbers had reached 2000. Initiating a programme of modernisation, an electric glost kiln was installed. A smaller script mark came into use around this time.

1948 An electric biscuit oven was installed.

1955 An infra-red dryer, cutting drying time from three-quarters of an hour to ten minutes was installed.

1958 Mr. A.L. Jackson joined as sales manager. In January the firm became Carlton Ware Limited. The Leaf range and the Windswept range were now in production, and motifs included Hazelnut, Convolvulus and Magnolia. By now a large export trade flourished.

1967 By now the impressed marks had reached 2694, and the firm was taken over by Arthur Wood & Son PLC. Designers during this period included Pamela Greeves (from 1975 to 1984) and Roger Michell and Danka Napiorkowska (the Walking Ware range).

1976 Salad Ware ceased, since new Health and Safety regulations prevented the continued use of the red colouring of the tomatoes.

1987 Renamed Carlton Ware and Kent, the factory was in the hands of a holding company County Potteries PLC.

1989 Into receivership in March, but a rescue bid launched in May by Grosvenor Ceramics Hardware PLC.

1990 The firm relaunched in February with a Centenary Vase.

1991 In the autumn production ceased, after just over a century of varied but mostly successful history.

BIBLIOGRAPHY

Art Deco Tableware by Judy Spours (Chapter 6) Ward Lock, 1988
A Collector's History of English Pottery by Griselda Lewis, Antique Collectors Club 1985
Dynamic Design, the British Pottery Industry 1940-1990 by Kathy Niblett, Stoke-on-Trent City Museum and Art Gallery. 1990
Collecting Carlton Ware by Sonia Roberts, Art & Antiques, 19th August. 1978
Carlton Ware in Perspective by David Berry, Antique Dealer & Collectors Guide, July 1981
Carlton Ware, Naturalistic Patterns of the 1930s and 1940s by Robert Stirling, Antique Collecting.
Collectors' Choice by Pat Watson, Antique Dealer & Collectors Guide, December 1991
Carlton Ware - Quality or Kitsch? by Pat Watson, Antique Bulletin, July 1992.
The Pottery Gazette and Glass Trade Review 1926, 1929, 1956 & 1958.

BEVERLEY

ART NOUVEAU
ART DECO

(Caption see page 44)

Visit our large shop in Central London for an
extensive range of 1920s and 1930s ceramics and
glass including Carlton Ware, Clarice Cliff, Shelley,
Susie Cooper and Keith Murray etc.

Monday-Thursday 11.00-7.00 — Friday and Saturday 9.30-7.00
Sundays by appointment

30 Church Street • Marylebone • London NW8
Telephone: 071-262 1576

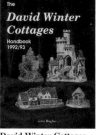

Notes